HOW TO STAY AWAKE DURING SEX

AND OTHER HANDY HINTS ON COPING WITH OLD AGE

BY MARTIN BAXENDALE

© Copyright 1991 Martin Baxendale
Published by Silent but Deadly Publications,
4 Catherine's Close, Stroud, Gloucestershire

ISBN 0-9513542-6-4

Printed in Britain by Stoate & Bishop (Printers) Ltd,
Cheltenham & Gloucester. Typesetting by Alpha Studio,
The Old Convent, Beeches Green, Stroud, Glos.

FOREWORD

The first signs of old age can creep up on you at any time. Don't let it catch you napping!

With the aid of this collection of invaluable tips and hints, the prospect of coping with advancing age will immediately lose its irrational fears and worries

Instead, you will find yourself positively looking forward to many happy years of decrepit wrinklieness, and the chance to put these pages of helpful advice into practice.

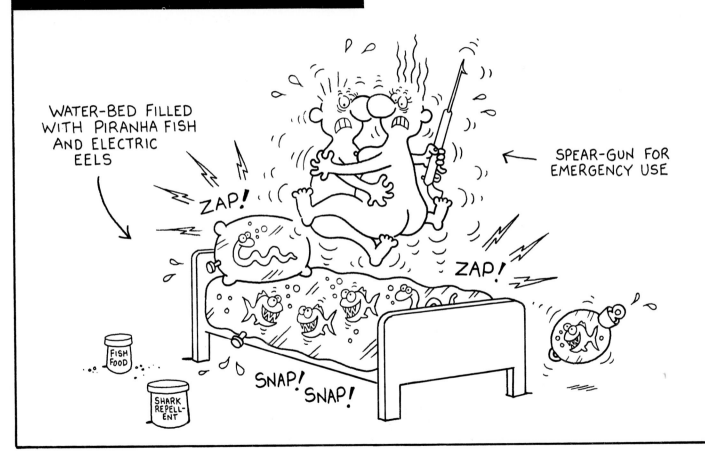

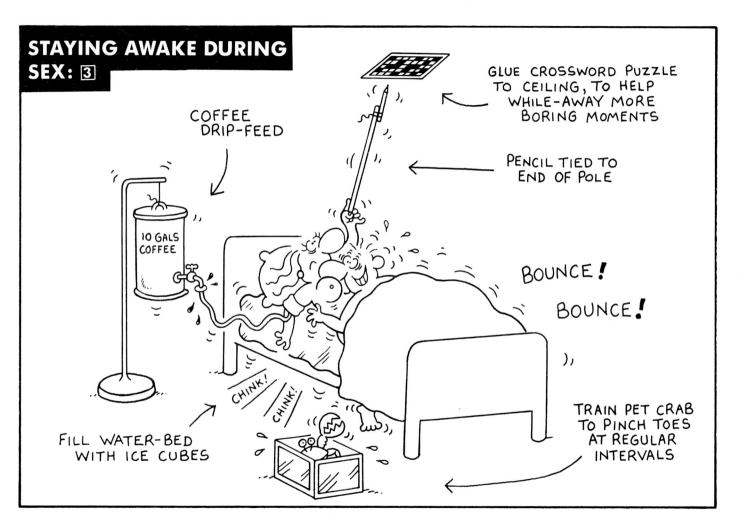

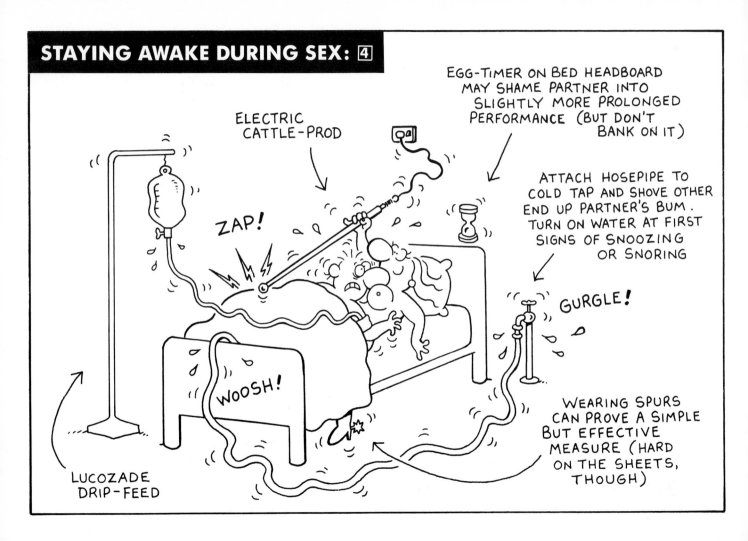

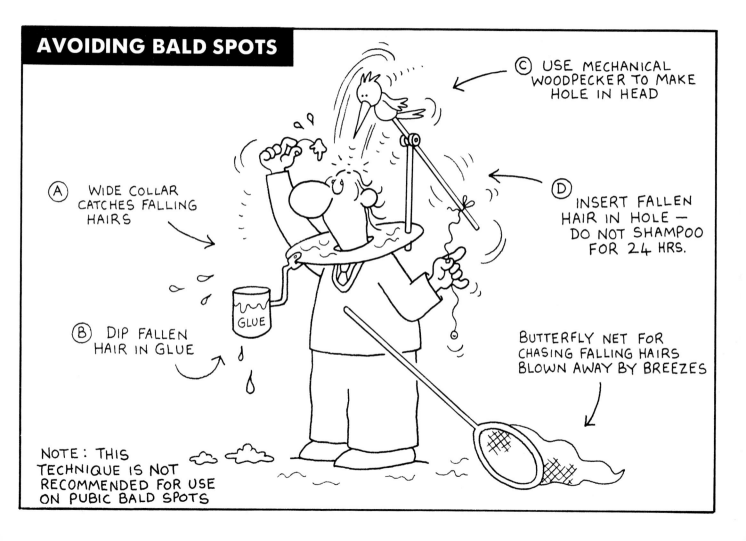

AVOIDING GREY HAIRS

ANGLED WING-MIRRORS FOR SPOTTING GREY HAIRS

MIRROR FOR SPOTTING GREY NOSE-HAIRS

EXPANDING TWEEZERS FOR PLUCKING GREY HAIRS

HIGH-PRESSURE SHOWER UNIT

50 GALLONS HAIR DYE / GRECIAN 2000/ LADY GRECIAN 2000, IN PRESSURIZED TANK

MIRROR FOR SPOTTING GREY PUBIC HAIRS

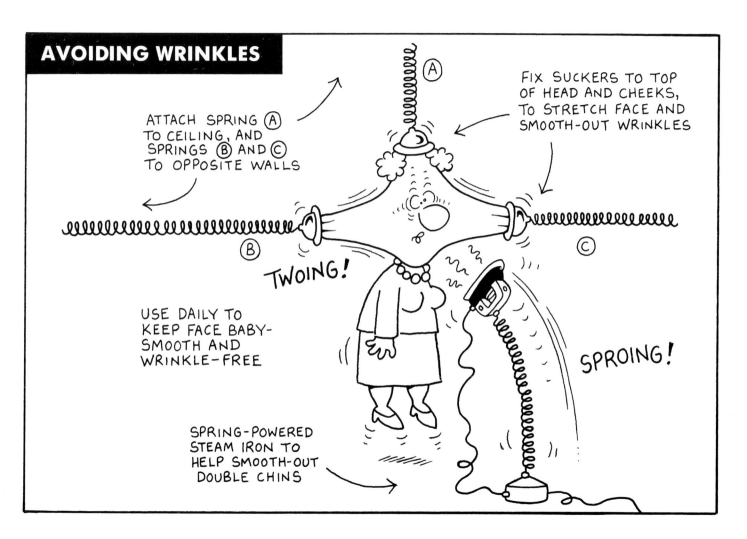

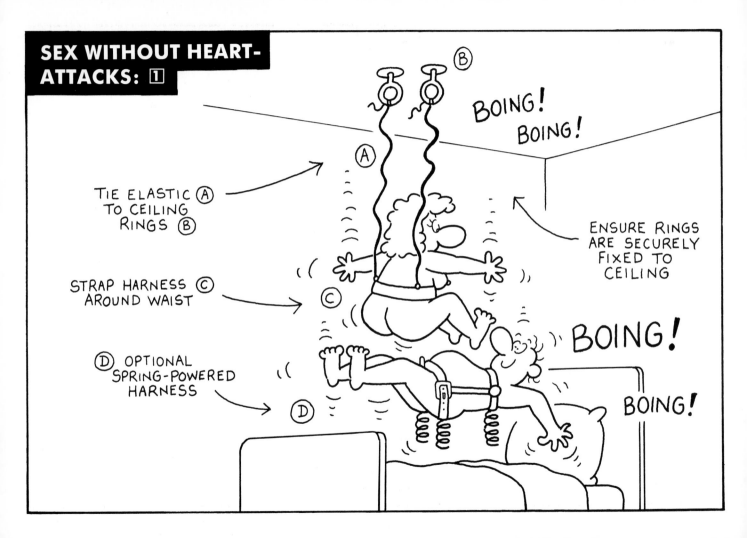

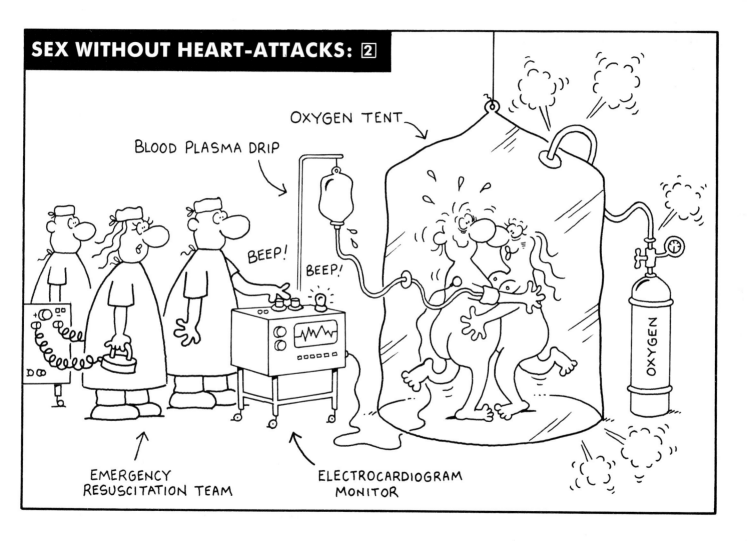

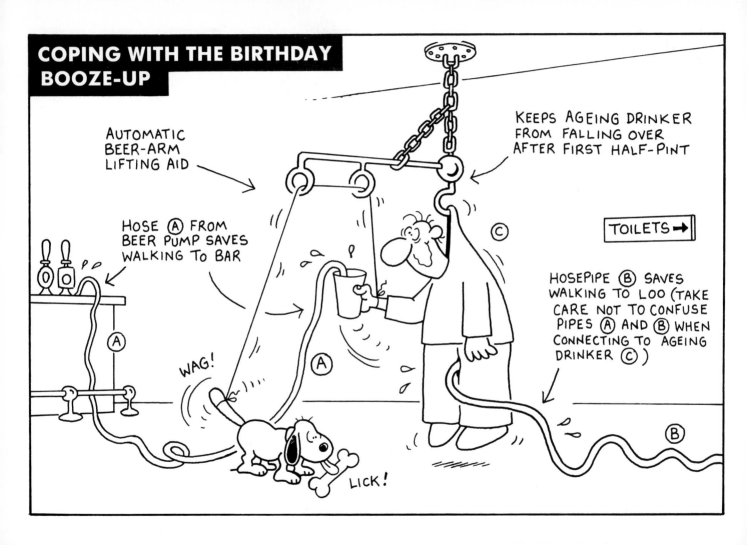

COPING WITH THE BIRTHDAY PARTY:
2 The birthday snogging session

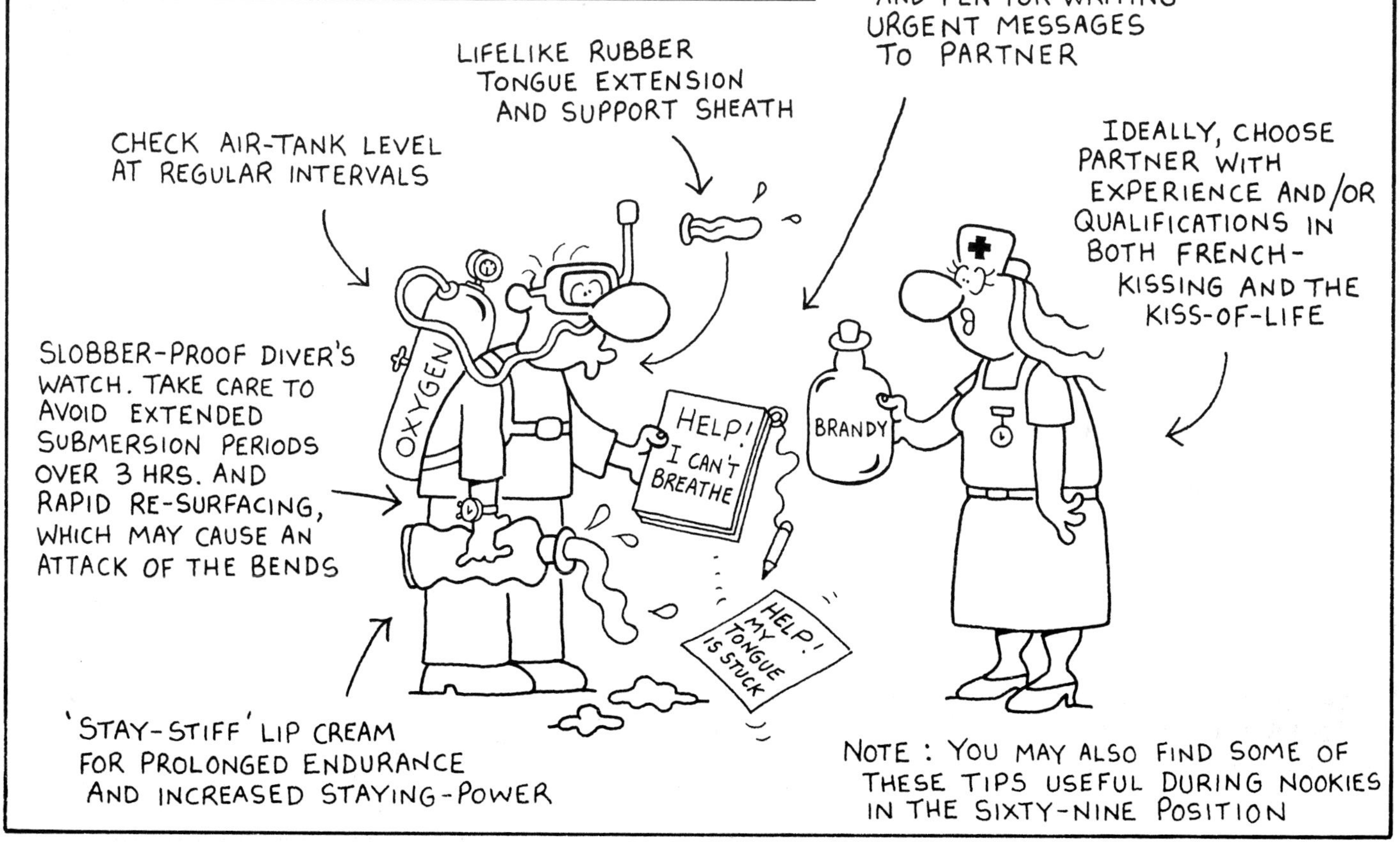

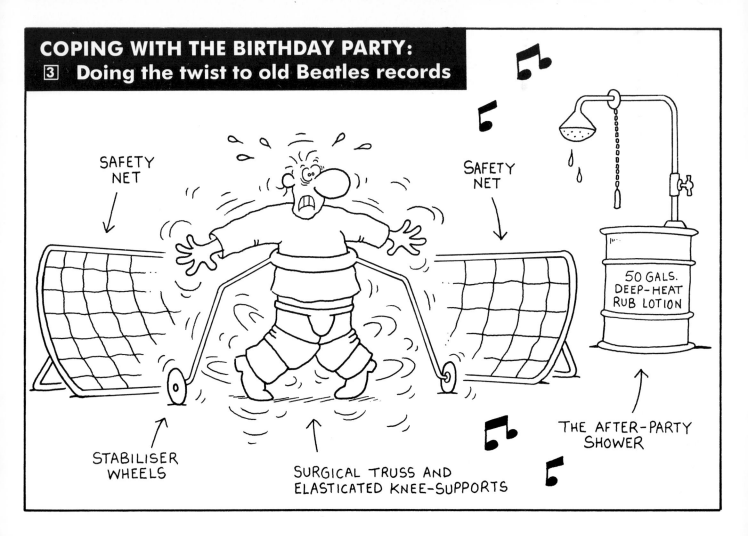

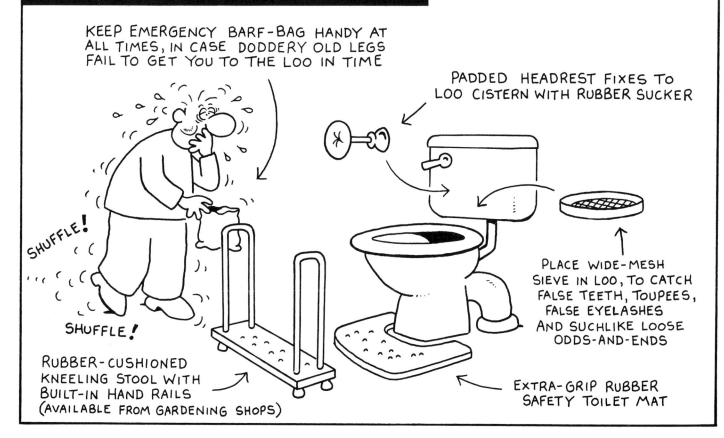

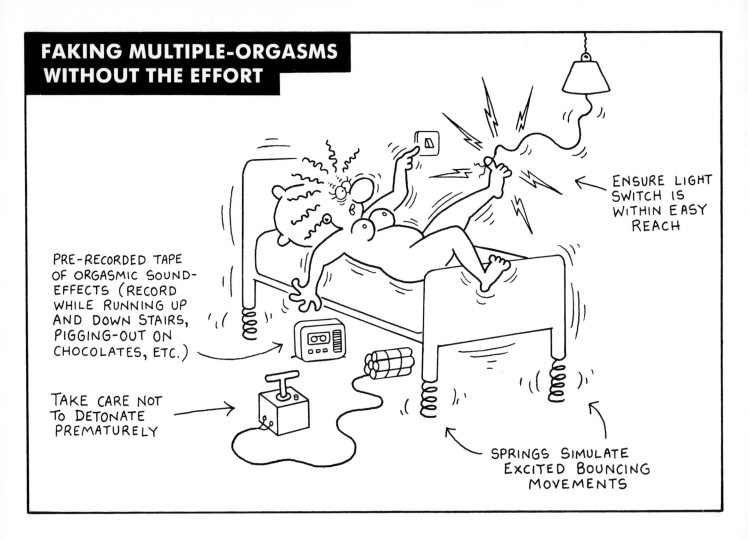

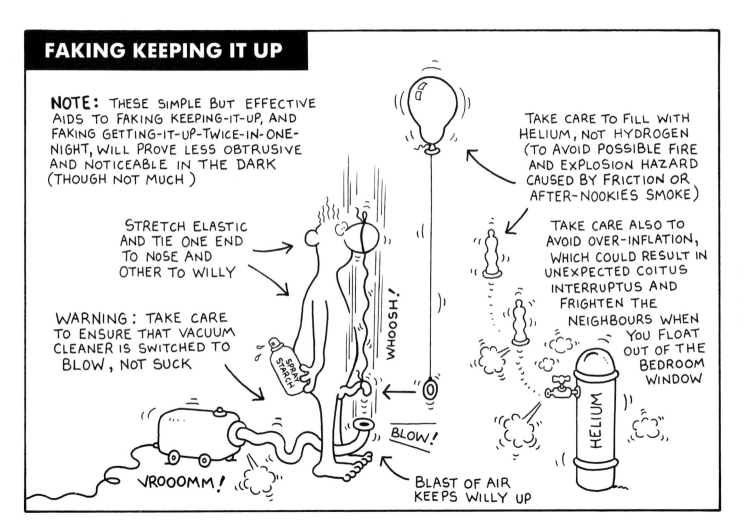

BEING A TRENDY OLDIE

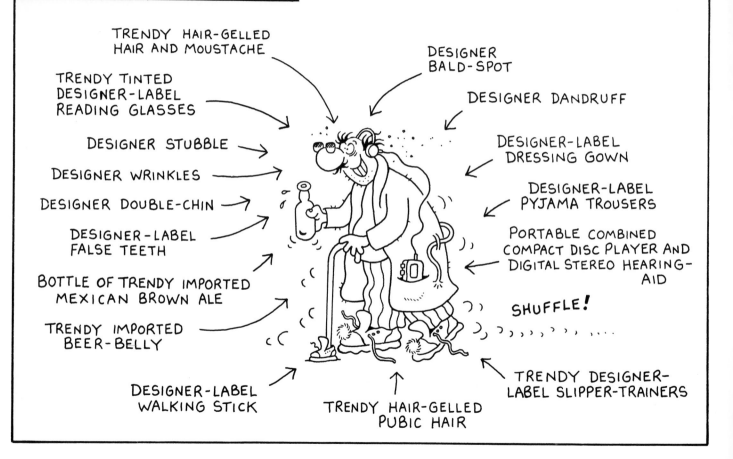

TRENDY HAIR-GELLED
HAIR AND MOUSTACHE

TRENDY TINTED
DESIGNER-LABEL
READING GLASSES

DESIGNER STUBBLE

DESIGNER WRINKLES

DESIGNER DOUBLE-CHIN

DESIGNER-LABEL
FALSE TEETH

BOTTLE OF TRENDY IMPORTED
MEXICAN BROWN ALE

TRENDY IMPORTED
BEER-BELLY

DESIGNER-LABEL
WALKING STICK

TRENDY HAIR-GELLED
PUBIC HAIR

DESIGNER
BALD-SPOT

DESIGNER DANDRUFF

DESIGNER-LABEL
DRESSING GOWN

DESIGNER-LABEL
PYJAMA TROUSERS

PORTABLE COMBINED
COMPACT DISC PLAYER AND
DIGITAL STEREO HEARING-
AID

SHUFFLE!

TRENDY DESIGNER-
LABEL SLIPPER-TRAINERS

HEALTHY-LIVING MADE EASY

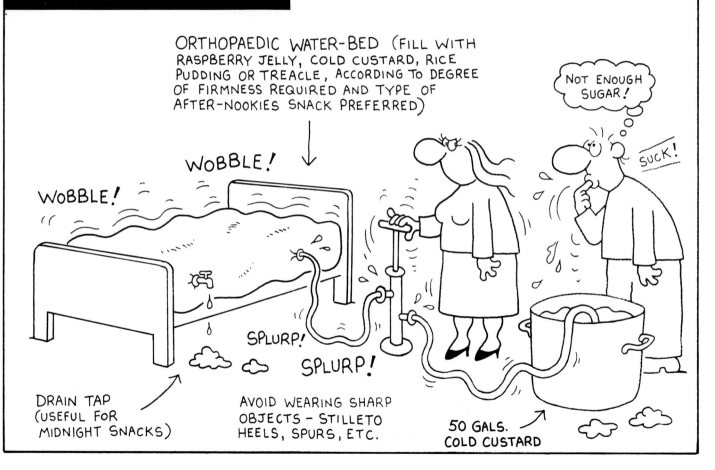

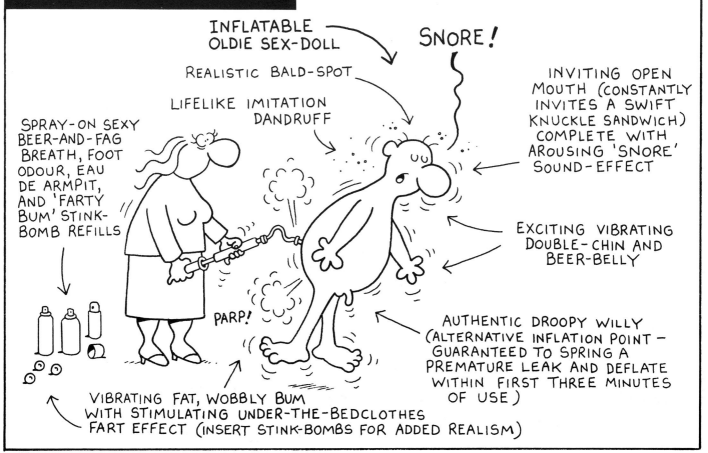

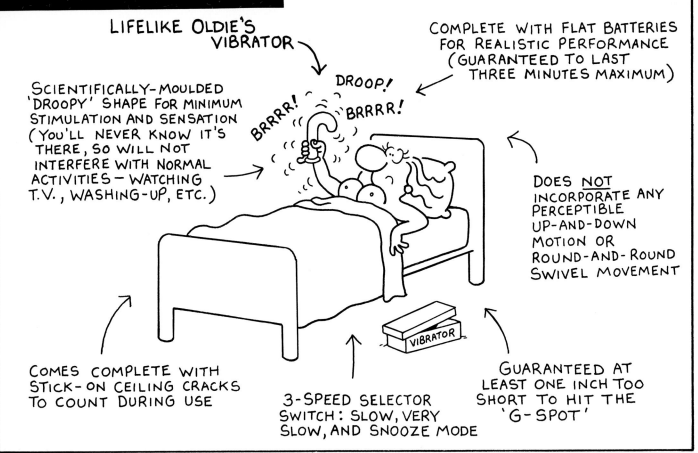

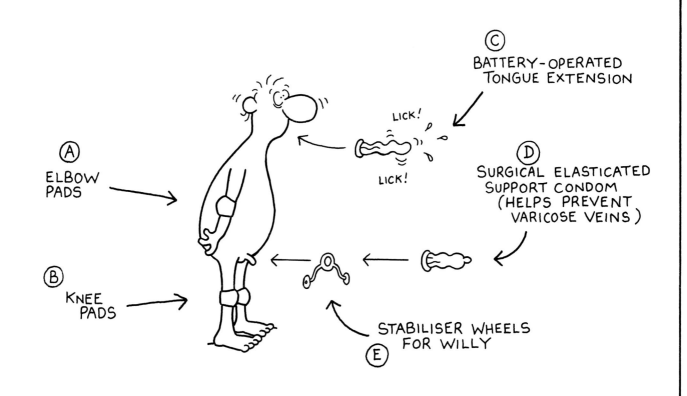

AN OLDIE'S GUIDE TO EROGENOUS ZONES

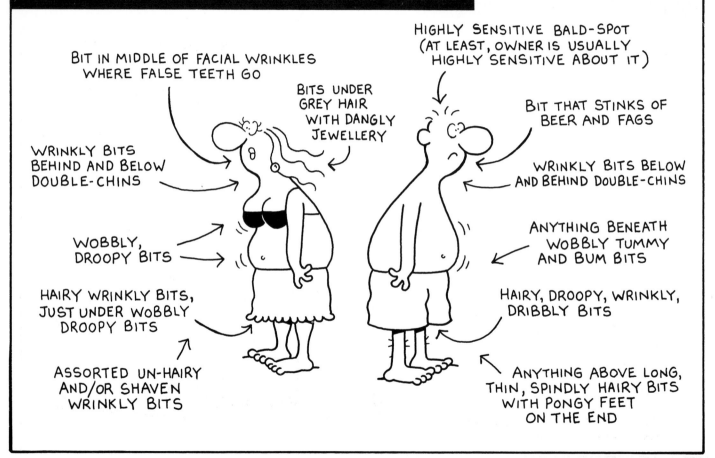

FOREPLAY FOR OLDIES

1 : DO WASHING-UP AND/OR PUT KIDS TO BED

2 : WORK OUT MORTGAGE REPAYMENTS AND/OR TRY TO BALANCE CHEQUE BOOK AND PLAN MONTHLY BUDGET

3 : HAVE A GOOD CRY

4 : COLLAPSE IN FRONT OF T.V.

5 : NIP DOWN TO LOCAL FOR QUICK PINT (USUALLY ONE PARTNER ONLY)

6 : EAT TAKE-AWAY, WATCH LATE FILM, FALL ASLEEP ON SETTEE

7 : MAKE HORLICKS/COCOA/DRINKING CHOCOLATE. TRY TO BALANCE CHEQUE BOOK, PLAN MONTHLY BUDGET, ETC.

8 : 11p.m. PARTNER (A) CLEANS TEETH AND GOES TO BED

9 : 1a.m. PARTNER (B) CLEANS TEETH AND GOES TO BED

10 : 1.05 a.m. PARTNER (A) OR (B) GETS UP TO FEED BABY/HAVE A PEE/TRY TO WORK OUT MONTHLY BUDGET/HAVE A GOOD CRY/DRINK BOTTLE OF SCOTCH OR BOTTLE OF GIN/TAKE OVERDOSE

11 : NOOKIES. IN THE UNLIKELY EVENT THAT YOU SHOULD ACTUALLY REACH THE STAGE OF HAVING NOOKIES, SEE ADVICE ON THE FOLLOWING PAGES

NOOKIES FOR OLDIES (A refresher course)

1 : VISIT DOCTOR FOR THOROUGH MEDICAL FITNESS CHECK-UP (BLOOD PRESSURE, ELECTROCARDIOGRAPH, POTENTIAL BREATHING PROBLEMS, HALITOSIS, ETC.)

2 : PRE-NOOKIES FITNESS TRAINING (MINIMUM THREE WEEKS JOGGING/EXERCISE BICYCLE/WEIGHT-TRAINING/PRESS-UPS/TONGUE-BUILDING EXERCISES)

3 : CHECK CORRECT AND SAFE FUNCTIONING OF BASIC EQUIPMENT AND ANY SURGICAL, KINKY OR ELECTRICAL APPLIANCES (INCLUDING BATTERY CHARGES) ESPECIALLY IF ANY OF THESE HAVE NOT BEEN USED FOR SOME TIME. ENSURE THAT ANY MAINS-POWERED ELECTRICAL APPLIANCES ARE FITTED WITH CIRCUIT-BREAKERS FOR ADDED SAFETY DURING USE, ESPECIALLY IN MOIST, DAMP AND DRIBBLY OPERATING CONDITIONS

4 : FOREPLAY (SEE PREVIOUS PAGE). NOTE :- EVENING-CLASS REFRESHER COURSES FOR MATURE STUDENTS MAY BE AVAILABLE AT MORE PROGRESSIVE LOCAL COLLEGES

A SENSUAL MASSAGE WITH DEEP-HEAT RUB CAN PROVE A STIMULATING AND HIGHLY EROTIC SEXUAL EXPERIENCE, WHILE AT THE SAME TIME SOOTHING OVER-STRAINED AGEING MUSCLES

5 : CHECK THAT YOU HAVE PARTNER. CHECK THAT PARTNER IS AWAKE/BREATHING/INFLATED

6 : COMMENCE BONKING (IT'S LIKE RIDING A BIKE - NO MATTER HOW LONG IT HAS BEEN, YOU'LL REMEMBER HOW. BUT DO EXPECT TO FALL OFF ONCE OR TWICE UNTIL YOU GET THE HANG OF IT AGAIN)

7 : WHEEZE, COUGH, GASP, STOP TO CATCH YOUR BREATH AND WAIT FOR THE ROOM TO STOP SPINNING ROUND

8 : COMPLAIN ABOUT BACK-ACHE. STOP FOR SENSUAL MUTUAL MASSAGE WITH DEEP-HEAT OINTMENT

9 : STOP FOR CUP OF TEA AND/OR A QUICK READ OF THAT BOOK YOU'VE BEEN TRYING TO FINISH FOR AGES

10 : REPEAT STEPS 5-9 UNTIL ONE OR OTHER PARTNER STARTS SNORING

11 : RECOVERY AND RECUPERATION: PRE- BOOK TIME OFF WORK, APPOINTMENT WITH OSTEOPATH/ORTHOPAEDIC SURGEON, FORTNIGHT IN REST-HOME